Vocal complete
SHEET MUSIC + BACKING TRACKS

COMPLETE Piano/Vocal/Guitar Sheet Music
Full-Band Backing Tracks on CDs
Tone 'N' Tempo Changer

F   **VOLUME 1**

JAZZ STANDARDS
DELUXE DOUBLE EDITION: 16 GREAT SONGS!

Contents

Produced by
Alfred Music Publishing Co., Inc.
P.O. Box 10003
Van Nuys, CA 91410-0003
alfred.com

Printed in USA.

ISBN-10: 0-7390-7907-7
ISBN-13: 978-0-7390-7907-2

Cover Photo: © 123rf.com / Aleksandr Frolov

Alfred Cares. Contents printed on 100% recycled paper.

ANYTHING GOES

Words and Music by
COLE PORTER

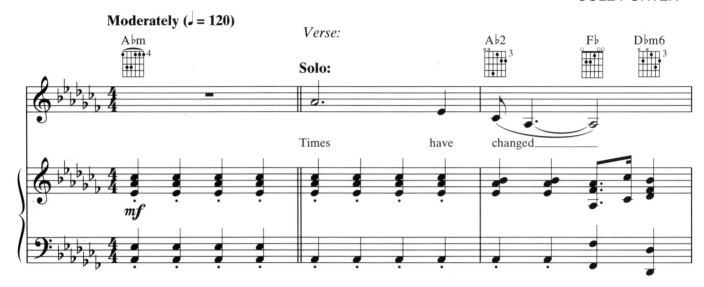

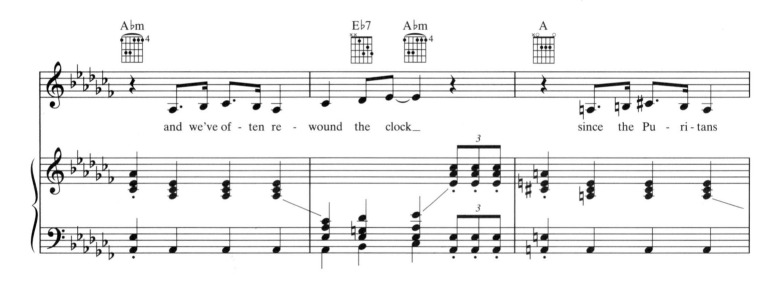

Anything Goes - 11 - 1

If to-day____ an-y shock they should try to stem,

'stead of land-ing on Plym-outh Rock, Plym-outh Rock should land on them.____ In

Relaxed 2-beat feel (♩ = 108)
Refrain 1:

old-en days a glimpse of stock-ing was looked on as some-thing shock-ing, but now, God

knows,_____ an-y-thing goes._____ Good

Anything Goes - 11 - 2

10

AT LAST

Lyrics by
MACK GORDON

Music by
HARRY WARREN

14

At Last - 5 - 2

BEWITCHED, BOTHERED AND BEWILDERED

Words by
LORENZ HART

Music by
RICHARD RODGERS

Bewitched, Bothered and Bewildered - 5 - 1

Moderately slow, with expression (♩ = 69)

Refrain:

CRY ME A RIVER

Words and Music by
ARTHUR HAMILTON

DON'T RAIN ON MY PARADE

Words by
BOB MERRILL

Music by
JULE STYNE

Don't Rain on My Parade - 8 - 1

DREAM A LITTLE DREAM OF ME

Lyrics by
GUS KAHN

Music by
FABIAN ANDRE and WILBUR SCHWANDT

38

MISTY

Words by
JOHNNY BURKE

Music by
ERROLL GARNER

Slowly, with expression

Misty - 3 - 1

EMBRACEABLE YOU

Music and Lyrics by
GEORGE GERSHWIN and IRA GERSHWIN

Embraceable You - 4 - 1

I GET A KICK OUT OF YOU

Words and Music by
COLE PORTER

MY FUNNY VALENTINE

Words by
LORENZ HART

Music by
RICHARD RODGERS

My Funny Valentine - 5 - 1

SUMMERTIME

Music and Lyrics by
GEORGE GERSHWIN, IRA GERSHWIN
and DuBOSE and DOROTHY HEYWARD

Summertime - 3 - 1

58

Summertime - 3 - 2

OVER THE RAINBOW

Lyrics by
E.Y. HARBURG

Music by
HAROLD ARLEN

Over the Rainbow - 4 - 1

62

Over the Rainbow - 4 - 3

SOMEONE TO WATCH OVER ME

Music and Lyrics by
GEORGE GERSHWIN
and IRA GERSHWIN

Someone to Watch Over Me - 6 - 1

THEY CAN'T TAKE THAT AWAY FROM ME

Music and Lyrics by
GEORGE GERSHWIN and IRA GERSHWIN

They Can't Take That Away From Me - 4 - 1

WHATEVER LOLA WANTS

Words and Music by
RICHARD ADLER and JERRY ROSS

Whatever Lola Wants - 5 - 1

76

WHEN I FALL IN LOVE

Words by
EDWARD HEYMAN

Music by
VICTOR YOUNG

ANYTHING GOES

(In the style of Eileen Rodgers)
Words and Music by COLE PORTER

Times have changed
and we've often rewound the clock
since the Puritans got a shock
when they landed on Plymouth Rock;

If today
any shock they should try to stem,
'stead of landing on Plymouth Rock,
Plymouth Rock would land on them.

In olden days a glimpse of stocking was
looked on as something shocking, but now, God knows,
anything goes.

Good authors, too, who once knew better words
now only use four letter words writing prose,
anything goes.

The world has gone mad today, and good's bad today,
and black's white today, and day's night today.
When most guys today, that women prize today,
are just silly gigolos:

So, though I'm not a great romancer,
I know that I'm bound to answer when you propose,
anything goes.

16-bar instrumental interlude

When grandmama's, whose age is eighty,
in nightclubs are getting matey with gigolos,
anything goes.

When mothers pack and leave poor father
because they decide they'd rather be tennis pros,
anything goes.

If driving fast cars you like, if low bars you like,
if old hymns you like, if bare limbs you like,
if Mae West you like, or me undressed you like,
why, nobody will oppose.

When ev'ry night, the set that's smart
is intruding in nudist parties in studios,
anything goes.

36-bar instrumental interlude

The world has gone mad today, and good's bad today,
and black's white today, and day's night today.
When most guys today, that women prize today,
are just silly gigolos:

So though I'm not a great romancer,
I know that I'm bound to answer when you propose,
anything goes.

If saying your pray'rs you like, if green pears you like,
if old chairs you like, if back stairs you like,
if love affairs you like, with young bears you like,
why, nobody will oppose.

And so though I'm not a great romancer,
I know that I'm bound to answer when you propose,
anything goes.

AT LAST

(In the style of Etta James)
Lyrics by MACK GORDON
Music by HARRY WARREN

At last,
my love has come along.
My lonely days are over
and life is like a song.

At last,
the skies above are blue.
My heart was wrapped up in clover
the night I looked at you.

I found a dream that I could speak to,
a dream that I can call my own.
I found a thrill to press my cheek to,
a thrill that I have never known.

When you smiled, you smiled,
oh, and then the spell was cast,
and here we are in heaven,
for you are mine at last.

BEWITCHED, BOTHERED, AND BEWILDERED

(In the style of Etta James)
Words by LORENZ HART
Music by RICHARD RODGERS

He's a fool and don't I know it.
But a fool can have his charms.
I'm in love and don't I show it,
like a babe in arms.

Love's the same old sad sensation.
Lately I've not slept a wink
since this halfpint imitation
put me on the blink.

I'm wild again! Beguiled again!
A simpering, whimpering child again.
Bewitched, bothered and bewildered am I.

Couldn't sleep and wouldn't sleep
when love came and told me I shouldn't sleep.
Bewitched, bothered and bewildered am I.

Lost my heart, but what of it?
He is cold, I agree.
He can laugh, but I love it,
although the laugh's on me.

I'll sing to him, each spring to him,
and long for the day when I'll cling to him.
Bewitched, bothered and bewildered am I.

Men are not a new sensation.
I've done pretty well, I think.
But this halfpint imitation
put me on the blink.

I've sinned a lot, I mean a lot!
But now I'm not sweet seventeen a lot.
Bewitched, bothered and bewildered am I.

CRY ME A RIVER
(In the style of Susan Boyle)
Words and Music by ARTHUR HAMILTON

Now you say you're lonely,
you cry the long night through.
Well, you can cry me a river, cry me a river;
I cried a river over you.

Now you say you're sorry
for being so untrue.
Well, you can cry me a river, cry me a river;
I cried a river over you.

You drove me, nearly drove me out of my head,
while you never shed a tear.
Remember, I remember all that you said;
told me love was too plebeian,
told me you were through with me, and,

Now you say you love me.
Well, just to prove that you do,
well, you can cry me a river, cry me a river;
I cried a river over you.

DON'T RAIN ON MY PARADE
(In the style of Barbra Streisand)
Words by BOB MERRILL
Music by JULE STYNE

Don't tell me not to live, just sit and putter.
Life's candy and the sun's a ball of butter.
Don't bring around a cloud to rain on my parade!

Don't tell me not to fly, I've simply got to.
If someone takes a spill, it's me and not you.
Who told you you're allowed to rain on my parade?

I'll march my band out, I'll beat my drum.
And if I'm fanned out, your turn at bat, sir,
at least I didn't fake it.
Hat, sir, I guess I didn't make it.

But whether I'm the rose of sheer perfection,
or freckle on the nose of life's complexion,
the cinder or the shiny apple of its eye.

I gotta fly once, I gotta try once,
only can die once. Right, sir?
Ooh, love is juicy, juicy and you see,
I gotta have my bite, sir!

Get ready for me, love, 'cause I'm a "comer."
I simply gotta march 'cause I'm a drummer.
Don't bring around a cloud to rain on my parade.
I'm gonna live and live now!

Get what I want, I know how.
One roll for the whole shebang!
One throw, that bell will go clang!
Eye on the target and wham!
One shot, one gun shot and bam!
Hey, Mister Arnstein, here I am!

I'll march my band out, I'll beat my drum.
And if I'm fanned out, your turn at bat, sir,
at least I didn't fake it.
Hat, sir! I guess I didn't make it!

Get ready for me, love, 'cause I'm a "comer."
I simply gotta march, my heart's a drummer.
Nobody, no, nobody is gonna rain on my parade!

DREAM A LITTLE DREAM OF ME

(In the style of Ella Fitzgerald)
Lyrics by GUS KAHN
Music by FABIAN ANDRE and WILBUR SCHWANDT

Stars shining bright above you,
night breezes seem to whisper, "I love you,"
birds singing in the sycamore tree,
dream a little dream of me.

Say "nightie-night" and kiss me.
Just hold me tight and tell me you'll miss me.
While I'm alone and blue as can be,
dream a little dream of me.

Stars fading but I linger on, dear,
still craving your kiss.
I'm longing to linger 'til dawn, dear,
just saying this:

Sweet dreams 'til sunbeams find you.
Sweet dreams that leave all worries behind you.
And in your dreams, whatever they be,
dream a little dream of me.

16-bar instrumental interlude

Stars fading but I linger on, dear,
still craving your kiss.
I'm longing to linger 'til dawn, dear,
just saying this:

Sweet dreams 'til sunbeams find you.
Sweet dreams that leave all worries behind you.
And in your dreams, whatever they be,
dream a little dream of me; dream of me.

EMBRACEABLE YOU

(In the style of Judy Garland)
Music and Lyrics by GEORGE GERSHWIN and IRA GERSHWIN

Embrace me, my sweet embraceable you.
Embrace me, you irreplaceable you.
Just one look at you, my heart grows tipsy in me.
You and you alone bring out the gypsy in me.

I love all the many charms about you;
above all I want my arms about you.
Don't be a naughty baby, come to mama,
come to mama, do!
My sweet embraceable you.

16-bar instrumental interlude

I love all the many charms about you;
above all I want my arms about you.
Don't be a naughty baby, come to mama,
come to mama, do!
My sweet embraceable you,
my sweet embraceable you.

I GET A KICK OUT OF YOU

(In the style of Ella Fitzgerald)
Words and Music by COLE PORTER

My story is much too sad to be told.
But practic'lly ev'rything leaves me totally cold.
The only exception I know is the case
when I'm out on a quiet spree,
fighting vainly the old ennui,
and I suddenly turn and see your fabulous face.

I get no kick from champagne,
mere alcohol doesn't thrill me at all.
So, tell me why should it be true that
I get a kick out of you?

Some get a kick from cocaine.
I'm sure that if I took even one sniff,
that would bore me terrific'lly too.
But I get a kick out of you.

I get a kick ev'ry time I see you're standing there before me.
I get a kick, though it's clear to me you
obviously don't adore me.

I get no kick in a plane.
Flying too high with some guy in the sky
is my idea of nothing to do.
Yet, I get a kick out of you.

I get a kick ev'ry time I see you're standing there before me.
I get a kick, though it's clear to me you
obviously don't adore me.

I get no kick in a plane.
Flying too high with some guy in the sky
is my idea of nothing to do.
Yet, I get a kick out of you.
I get a kick out of you.

MISTY

(In the style of Ella Fitzgerald)
Words by JOHNNY BURKE
Music by ERROLL GARNER

Look at me;
I'm as helpless as a kitten up a tree,
and I feel like I'm clinging to a cloud.
I can't understand; I get misty
just holding your hand.

Walk my way,
and a thousand violins begin to play,
or it might be the sound of your hello,
that music I hear. I get misty
the moment you're near.

You can say that you're leading me on,
but it's just what I want you to do.
Don't you notice how hopelessly I'm lost?
That's why I'm following you.

On my own,
would I wander through this wonderland alone,
never knowing my right foot from my left,
my hat from my glove? I'm too misty
and too much in love.

I'm too misty and too much in love.

MY FUNNY VALENTINE

(In the style of Ella Fitzgerald)
Words by LORENZ HART
Music by RICHARD RODGERS

Behold the way our fine feathered friend his virtue doth parade.
Thou knowest not, my dimwitted friend, the picture thou hast made.
Thy vacant brow and thy tossled hair conceal thy good intent.
Thou noble, upright, truthful, sincere, and slightly dopey gent.

You're my funny valentine, sweet comic valentine,
you make me smile with my heart.
Your looks are laughable, unphotographable, yet,
you're my fav'rite work of art.

Is your figure less than Greek?
Is your mouth a little weak?
When you open it to speak, are you smart?

But don't change a hair for me,
not if you care for me.
Stay, little valentine, stay.
Each day is Valentine's Day.

Is your figure less than Greek?
Is your mouth a little weak?
When you open it to speak, are you smart?

But don't change a hair for me,
not if you care for me.
Stay, little valentine, stay.
Each day is Valentine's Day.

OVER THE RAINBOW

(In the style of Judy Garland)
Lyric by E. Y. HARBURG
Music by HAROLD ARLEN

Somewhere over the rainbow, way up high,
there's a land that I heard of once in a lullaby.
Somewhere over the rainbow, skies are blue,
and the dreams that you dare to dream really do come true.

Someday I'll wish upon a star
and wake up where the clouds are far behind me.
Where troubles melt like lemon drops,
away above the chimney tops, that's where you'll find me.

Somewhere over the rainbow, bluebirds fly.
Birds fly over the rainbow; why then, oh, why can't I?
If happy little bluebirds fly
beyond the rainbow, why, oh, why can't I?

SOMEONE TO WATCH OVER ME

(In the style of Ella Fitzgerald)
Music and Lyrics by GEORGE GERSHWIN and IRA GERSHWIN

There's a saying old, says that love is blind.
Still we're often told, "Seek and ye shall find."
So, I'm going to seek a certain lad I've had in mind.
Looking ev'rywhere, haven't found him yet.

He's the big affair I cannot forget.
Only man I ever think of with regret.
I'd like to add his initial to my monogram.
Tell me, where is the shepherd for this lost lamb?

There's a somebody I'm longing to see.
I hope that he turns out to be
someone who'll watch over me.

I'm a little lamb who's lost in the wood.
I know I could always be good
to one who'll watch over me.

Although he may not be the man
some girls think of as handsome,
to my heart, he carries the key.

Won't you tell him, please, to put on some speed,
follow my lead. Oh, how I need
someone to watch over me.

8-bar instrumental interlude

Won't you tell him, please, to put on some speed,
follow my lead. Oh, how I need
someone to watch over me, someone to watch over me.

SUMMERTIME

(In the style of Ella Fitzgerald)
Words and Music by GEORGE GERSHWIN, IRA GERSHWIN, and DuBOSE and DOROTHY HEYWARD

Summertime, and the livin' is easy,
fish are jumpin',
an' the cotton is high.

Oh, yo' daddy's rich,
an' yo' ma is good-lookin',
so hush, little baby,
don' you cry.

One of these mornin's
you're goin' to rise up singin',
then you'll spread yo' wings
an' you'll take the sky.

But till that mornin'
there's a-nothin' can harm you
with Daddy an' Mammy standin' by.

THEY CAN'T TAKE THAT AWAY FROM ME

(In the style of Ella Fitzgerald)
Music and Lyrics by GEORGE GERSHWIN and IRA GERSHWIN

The way you wear your hat,
the way you sip your tea,
the mem'ry of all that, no, no,
they can't take that away from me.

The way your smile just beams,
the way you sing off key,
the way you haunt my dreams, no, no,
they can't take that away from me.

We may never, never meet again
on the bumpy road to love.
Still I'll always, always keep the mem'ry of

the way you hold your knife,
the way we danced 'til three,
the way you've changed my life, no, no,
they can't take that away from me.
No, they can't take that away from me!

16-bar instrumental interlude

We may never, never meet again
on the bumpy road to love.
Still I'll always, always keep the mem'ry of

the way you hold your knife,
the way we danced 'til three,
the way you've changed my life, no, no,
they can't take that away from me.

No, they can't take that a way,
they can't take that away,
no, they can't take that away from me.

WHATEVER LOLA WANTS

(In the style of Sarah Vaughan)
Words and Music by RICHARD ADLER and JERRY ROSS

Whatever Lola wants, Lola gets,
and, little man, little Lola wants you.
Make up your mind to have no regrets.
Recline yourself, resign yourself, you're through.

I always get what I aim for.
And your heart and soul is what I came for.
Whatever Lola wants, Lola gets.
Take off your coat, don't you know you can't win.

You're no exception to the rule.
I'm irresistible, you fool. Give in.
Whatever Lola wants, Lola gets.

I always get what I aim for.
And your heart and soul is what I came for.
Whatever Lola wants, Lola gets.
Take off your coat, don't you know you can't win.

You're no exception to the rule.
I'm irresistible, you fool. Give in,
give in, give in.

WHEN I FALL IN LOVE

(In the style of Linda Ronstadt)
Words by EDWARD HEYMAN
Music by VICTOR YOUNG

When I fall in love,
it will be forever,
or I'll never fall in love.

In a restless world like this is,
love is ended before it's begun,
and too many moonlight kisses
seem to melt in the warmth of the sun.

When I give my heart,
it will be completely,
or I'll never give my heart.

And the moment I can feel
that you feel that way, too,
is when I'll give my heart to you.